The Skip

for

Annie Butler Wandell

J
398.8
B

3/74

Rope Book

collected by *Francelia Butler*
illustrated by *Gail E. Haley*

with an introduction
by *Phyllis McGinley*

THE DIAL PRESS INC.

NEW YORK

Introduction

Children are the great traditionalists. The kingdom of which they are citizens for so brief a time is violently conservative and its speech, its customs alter slowly if at all.

Particularly this is true in their play. The dolls, balls, stick of this century differ only slightly from the sticks, balls, dolls of young Babylonians. Tag was played in the Rome of Augustus and under-aged Athenians 2500 years ago flew their kites in the gusty March air. I do not know when or how the game of skip-rope began but I presume its lineage is equally honorable and ancient. Certainly English children were hopping and bounding "now on one foot, now on two" before their descendents moved across the Atlantic to America. And as they leaped, their folk-dance was performed to ritual rhythms very much like the ones in this book—sometimes to exactly the same jingles.

No child invented the rhymes. As conservatives, children seldom invent. They adapt, instead, warping into their own argot the ballads, street songs, nursery lilts and political doggeral of every era. And by oral tradition the songs go on from generation to generation. Thus we have eight-year-olds nowadays who have never heard of Theodore Roosevelt chanting, still, "Teddy Bear, Teddy Bear, touch your shoe." I have even overheard them sing it with such a turn-of-the-century finale as "Teddy Bear, Teddy Bar, 23 skidoo!" My mother and my grandmother knew that riposte, yet (although this collection does not contain it, having brighter treasures to display) it was popular as late as last April with the nimblest jumpers of my neighborhood.

Thus we have, also, springtime children hopping to something as nearly up-to-date as "Salome was a dancer, she danced before the king," or "Dagwood, Blondie, went downtown," and a moment later to something as sly and classic as "I had a little nut tree," unchanged by a syllable since the 17th century.

Probably all grown-ups who read the rhymes assembled here will recall different versions singular to their own locality. But no one, surely, can turn the pages without nostalgia, remembering the lost pleasures of the whirling rope, the braids or the curls bobbing on the neck, the delirious flurry of "Salt, vinegar, mustard, PEPPER !".

They must also feel consoled.

For in a veering world with only death and taxes supposedly constant, it is heartening to know that, fifty years from now if the planet is still in orbit, our posterity will be shouting as they jump, "Intry, mintry, cutry corn, apple seed and apple thorn," a refrain as old as the English language. Childhood's kingdom has steadfast laws.

—PHYLLIS McGINLEY

Johnny Maloney

Johnny Maloney,
Stick, stick stony,
Highballa, o balla,
Johnny Maloney.

Dagwood and Blondie

Dagwood, Blondie went downtown,
Blondie bought an evening gown,
Dagwood bought a pair of shoes,
Alexander bought the Evening News.
This is what it said:
Close your eyes and count to ten:

1—2—3—4—till you miss.

Amos 'n Andy

Amos 'n Andy
    Sugar 'n Candy
        I pop in.

Amos 'n Andy
    Sugar 'n Candy
        I pop down.

Amos 'n Andy
    Sugar 'n Candy
        I pop up.

Amos 'n Andy
    Sugar 'n Candy
        I pop out.

Blue Bells

Bluebells, cockle shells,
Evie ivy over;
My father is a butcher,
My mother cuts the meat,
And I'm a little hot dog
That runs around the street.
How many hot dogs can you eat?

1—2—3—4—till you miss.

On The Hilltop Stands a Lady

On the hilltop stands a lady,
Who she is I do not know.
All she wears is gold and silver,
And she needs a nice new maid.
So run out Miss Ruby,
And jump in Miss Lois.

Use the names of your own friends. Someone runs out
and someone new jumps in under the rope.

I Told Ma

I told Ma,
Ma told Pa,
Johnny got a lickin',
Ha! Ha! Ha!

     How many lickin's did he get?
     1—2—3—4—till you miss.

Marge Drank Some Milk

Marge drank some milk,
Marge drank some beer,
Marge drank some other things
that made her feel so queer.

A moakly went the milk,
A moakly went the beer,
A moakly went the other things
that made her feel so queer.

Reuben, Reuben

Reuben, Reuben, I've been thinkin'
What in the world have you been drinkin'?
Is it whisky? Is it wine?
Oh my gosh, it's turpentine!

"Skin" this one: that means keep going as fast as
you can till you miss.

Down in the Valley

Down in the valley where the green grass
 grows,
There sat Susie as sweet as a rose.
She sang, she sang, she sang so sweet,
Along came Tommy and kissed her on
 the cheek.
 How many kisses did she receive?
 1—2—3—4—till you miss.

Changing Bedrooms

Changing bedrooms Number one!
 (Two girls change places while jumping.)
Changing bedrooms Number two!
 (Change places again.)
Changing bedrooms Number three!
 (Change places again.)
Changing bedrooms Number four!

(Change places again. The girl in front jumps out
and another jumps in.)

Charlie Chaplin Went to France

Charlie Chaplin went to France
To teach the girlies how to dance.
Heel, toe, around we go,
Heel, toe, around we go.
Salute to the Captain,
Bow to the Queen,
Touch the bottom
Of a submarine, and
KEEP THE KETTLE BOILING!

Here one jumper skips out and another jumps in and starts skipping, repeating the rhyme from the beginning.

Charlie Chaplin

Charlie Chaplin
Sat on a pin.
How many inches
Did it go in?

1—2—3—4—till you miss.

FRANCE

The Clown

The clown in his store
  (Arlequin dans sa boutique)
On the palace stair
  (Sur les marches du palais)
Teaching numbers
  (Enseignant l'arithmétique)
To his pupils there.
  (A tous ses petits sujets):

  1—2—3—4— till you miss.

Red, White, and Yellow

Red, white, and yellow.
Have you got a fellow?
Yes, no, maybe so
Yes, no, maybe so . . . till you miss.

Fudge, Fudge

Fudge, fudge, call the judge,
Mama's got a baby.
Ain't no girl; ain't no boy,
Just a plain old baby.
Wrap it up in tissue paper,
Put it on the elevator.
> *First floor—Miss!*
> *Second floor—Miss!*
> *Third floor—Miss!*
> *Fourth floor—*

KICK   IT   OUT   THE   DOOR!

My Mom and Your Mom

My mother and your mother
Lives across the way.
Every night they have a fight
And this is what they say:
Acka backa soda cracker
Acka backa boo
Acka backa soda cracker
Out goes you!

Mabel, Mabel

Mabel, Mabel, set the table.
Don't forget the salt—vinegar—mustard—
PEPPER!

At the word "pepper", turn the rope as fast as you can till the jumper misses.

Grace, Grace;

Grace, Grace,
Dressed in lace,
Went upstairs
To powder her face.
How many boxes did she use?
1—2—3—4—till you miss.

Virginia Had a Baby

Virginia had a baby,
She named it Tiny Tim,
She put it in the washtub,
To teach it how to swim.
It floated up the river,
It floated down the lake,
And now Virginia's baby
Has the bellyache!

Ke Clip, Ke Clop

Ke clip, ke clop, ke clip, ke clop,
*   A hundred times before we stop,*
And if we trip (as trip we may),
*   We'll try again some other day!*
        1—2—3—4—up to ninety-nine.*
*It's bad luck to jump to one hundred.

Pop, Pop, Pop

Pop, Pop, Pop,
The girls are calling
For Daisy to come in.
*   Daisy is the one*
*   Who is going to have the fun,*
*   So we don't need—Hattie!*
Use the names of your own friends. The first one in
is the first one out.

HOUSE FOR RENT
INQUIRE WITHIN
*When I move out
Let Katie move in.*
When one jumper moves out, next jumper moves in.

Apple on a Stick

*Apple on a stick
Makes me sick.
Tummy ache, tummy ache,*
2—4—6—8—till you miss.

I Had a Little Brother

I had a little brother,
His name was Tiny Tim.
I put him in the washtub
To teach him how to swim.
He drank up all the water,
He ate up all the soap.
He died last night
With a bubble in his throat.

I had a little brother and his name was
        Johnny,
He played in the meadow where the frogs
        croaked clear,
He ran through the meadow with a song
        on his tongue.
And he picked a few flowers for his mother.
        How many flowers did he gather?
        1—2—3—4—till you miss.

Johnny Over the Ocean

Johnny over the ocean,
Johnny over the sea,
Johnny broke a milk bottle,
And blamed it on me.

The Devil Flew

The Devil flew
*   from north to south*
with Miss Hooker
*   in his mouth,*
And when he found
*   she was a fool,*
He dropped her on
*   the Cherrydale School.*

All In Together Girls

All in together, girls,
No mind the weather, girls,
See the teacher tapping on the winder.
January, February, March ... till you miss.

This one is good for jumping "Double Dutch," that
is, with two long ropes turning in opposite directions.

Fortunes

I love my Papa, that I do,
*   And Mama says she loves him, too,*
But Papa says he fears some day
*   With some bad man I'll run away.*
Who will I marry?
Rich man, poor man, beggar man, thief,
Doctor, lawyer, merchant, chief,
Tinker, tailor, soldier, sailor.
How will I dress?
Silk, satin, calico, rags.
What kind of ring will I wear?
Diamond, emerald, ruby, pearl.
What kind of house will I live in?
Big house, little house, pig pen, barn.
How many children will I have?

1—2—3—4—till you miss.

Annie Cum Banny

Annie, cum banny,
Tee alligo skanny,
Tee-legged, tie-legged,
Bow-legged Annie.

Ice Cream, Soda Water

Ice cream, soda water, gingerale, pop,
Tell me the initials of your sweetheart:
A— B— C— D— and miss on the initials of your
sweetheart.

I Had a Little Nut Tree

I had a little nut tree,
Nothing would it bear
But a silver nutmeg
And a golden pear.
The King of Spain's daughter
Came to visit me,
And all because
Of my little nut tree.

This rhyme, a favorite with jumpers, is one of the oldest and naughtiest. Legend has it that it was the veiled protest of the people to Henry VIII's courtship of Catherine of Aragon and later, to the future King Charles I's interest in the Infanta of Spain. The "silver nutmeg" contained a nutmeg and a little grater and was a handy gadget (gallants carried them) for spicing hot toddies.

Intry, Mintry

Intry mintry cutry corn,
Apple seed and apple thorn,
Wire brier limber lock,
Three geese in a flock,
One flew east and one flew west,
And one flew over the cuckoo's nest!

I Had a Little Monkey

I had a little monkey.
I sent him to the country.
I fed him on gingerbread.
He jumped out the winder,
And broke his little finger.
And now my monkey's dead.

One, Two, Three

One, two, three,
Cat's in the well.
Four, five, six,
Pick up sticks.
Seven, eight, nine,
Cut the clothesline.
Nine, ten, eleven,
Cat's gone to heaven.

Lady In a Boat

A lady in a boat
With a red petticoat
*And her name is—*MISS!

Old Man Dazy

Old man Dazy
He went crazy.
Up the ladder,
Down the ladder,
I say STOOP!
Stoop three counts, then repeat.

Raspberry Jam

Raspberry, Rasberry, Raspberry Jam.
Tell me the initials of my old man.
A— B— C— D— till you miss.

Down the Mississippi

Down the Mississippi
Where the steamboats PUSH!
If somebody is hogging the rope, jump in and push
him out.

Last Night

Last night, the night before,
A lemon and a pickle came a knockin'
at my door.
When I went down to let them in,
They hit me over the head with a rollin' pin.
This is what they said to me:
Lady, lady turn around.
Lady, lady touch the ground.
Lady, lady show your shoe.
Lady, lady how old are you?
1—2—3—4—till you miss.

Teddy Bear, Teddy Bear,
*   turn around,*
Teddy Bear, Teddy Bear,
*   touch the ground,*
Teddy Bear, Teddy Bear,
*   shine your shoe,*
Teddy Bear, Teddy Bear,
*   that will do.*
Teddy Bear, Teddy Bear,
*   go upstairs,*
Teddy Bear, Teddy Bear,
*   say your prayers,*
Teddy Bear, Teddy Bear,
*   turn out the light,*
Teddy Bear, Teddy Bear,
*   say good night.*
Teddy Bear hop on one foot, one foot,
Teddy Bear hop on two feet, two feet,
Teddy Bear hop on three feet, three feet,
Teddy Bear hop right out.

Way Down South

Way down south where the sharecroppers
*   grow,*
I saw some croppers croppin' to and fro.
They cropped some peas, they cropped
*   some beans,*
They cropped right up to the tops of
*   the trees.*
Up in Virginia where the grass grows
*   green,*
I saw a cute boy in a flyin' machine.
The machine went up, the boy came down,
He landed in the middle of Arling-town.
In North Carolina where tobacco is
*   the crop,*
I saw an old hen go flippity flop.
She flipped up once, she flipped down
*   twice,*

She landed in the middle of a bowl of rice.
Down in South Carolina where the
       'ristocrats grow,
I saw three birdies sittin' all in a row.
The crow said "caw", the cat said "cree",
       the finch said
"Now you all quit a mockin' me.
Cree, craw, cree, cree, craw, cree,
You all quit a mockin' me."
Way down in Georgia where the peach
       trees blow,
I saw a little girl standin' on her tiptoe,
She tipped to the east, she tipped to
       the west,
She tipped to the boy that she loved best!
How many tippies did she make?
       5— 10— 15— 20— till you miss.

Mother, mother, I am ill,
*   Call for the Doctor over the hill:*
First came the Doctor,
*   Then came the Nurse,*
*   Then came the lady with the*
*   Alligator purse.*
*   Out went the Doctor,*
*   Out went the Nurse,*
* Out went the Lady with the*
Alligator purse.

Little Miss Pink

Little Miss Pink
*   Dressed in blue*
Died last night
*   At quarter past two.*
Before she died
*   She told me this:*
"When I jump rope,
*   I always miss!"*
*   Did she go up or down?*
"Up— down— up— down— up— down—" till you miss.

What are you doing here, Sir?
Drinking up the beer, Sir.
Where did you get the beer, Sir?
It wasn't far nor near, Sir.
    Yes Sir, no Sir,
      I must be on my way, Sir.
Where did you leave your cane, Sir?
Down in Lover's Lane, Sir.
What were you doing there, Sir?
None of your affair, Sir.
    Yes Sir, no Sir,
      I must be on my way, Sir.
Why do you speak so bold, Sir?
Because I have a cold, Sir.
Where did you get your cold, Sir?
Up at the North Pole, Sir.
    Yes Sir, no Sir,
      I must be on my way, Sir.
Where do you go to church, Sir?
Down by yonder birch, Sir.
Perhaps we then shall meet, Sir.
If I must rest my feet, Sir.
    Yes Sir, no Sir,
      I must be on my way, Sir.

Have you a horse to ride, Sir?
I'm sitting on its hide, Sir.
But no mount I see, Sir.
Its hide is sewed on me, Sir.
> *Yes Sir, no Sir,*
> > *I must be on my way, Sir.*
When will you be gone, Sir?
At the crack of dawn, Sir.
Who will let you out, Sir?
My musket good and stout, Sir.
> *Yes Sir, no Sir,*
> > *I must be on my way, Sir.*
Pray, what is your name, Sir?
My name is:

Now jump the letters of your own name.

Salome

Salome was a dancer,
She danced before the King.
She danced hanky-panky
And she shimmied everything.
The King said, "Salome,
You can't do that in here!"
Salome said "Baloney!"
And kicked the chandelier!

Butterfly, Butterfly

Butterfly, butterfly, fly around.
Butterfly, butterfly, dip to the ground.
Butterfly, butterfly, fold your wings tight.
Butterfly, butterfly, flit out of sight!